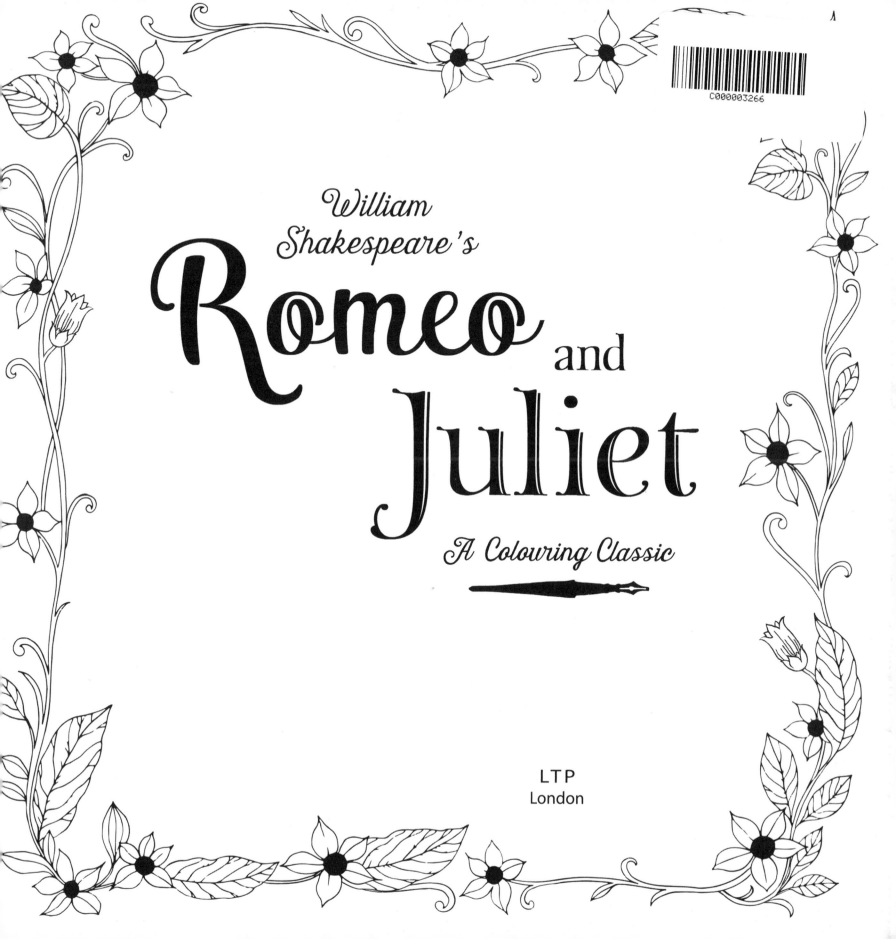

William Shakespeare's

Romeo and Juliet

A Colouring Classic

LTP
London

To Heracles ~ R M

For my wonderful family, lots of love Bethan ~ B J

LTP

1 The Coda Centre, 189 Munster Road, London SW6 6AW

www.littletiger.co.uk

First published in Great Britain 2016

Embark on a unique visual journey through William Shakespeare's Romeo and Juliet.

Each lovingly crafted spread includes a classic quotation from the play and illuminates central motifs such as fate, family and honour, not to mention marriage, love and untimely death. Delve into the Apothecary's bag as you discover the herbs and potions of the Renaissance, using the fascinating guide at the back of the book.

Add colour to intricate patterns and beautiful scenes inspired by the play, and let yourself be transported to Shakespeare's Italy.

The stage is set . . .

In fair Verona, where we lay our scene,

Capulet

From ancient grudge break to new mutiny,

Where civil blood makes civil hands unclean.

Montague

From forth the fatal loins of these two foes

A pair of star-cross'd lovers take their life,

'...if you be not of the house
of Montagues, I pray, come and crush a cup of wine.'
Servant

'Thou wast the prettiest babe that e'er I nursed:

An I might live to see thee married once,

I have my wish.'

Nurse

'You are a lover; borrow Cupid's wings,

And soar with them above a common bound.'

Mercutio

'You are welcome, gentlemen! come, musicians, play.'
Capulet

'I fear, too early: for my mind misgives
Some consequence yet hanging in the stars . . .'
Romeo

'And palm to palm is holy palmers' kiss.'
Juliet

'My only love sprung from my only hate!'

Juliet

'But, soft! what light through yonder window breaks?

It is the east, and Juliet is the sun.

Arise, fair sun, and kill the envious moon,

Who is already sick and pale with grief,

That thou her maid art far more fair than she.'

Romeo

'O Romeo, Romeo! wherefore art thou Romeo?

Deny thy father and refuse thy name;

Or, if thou wilt not, be but sworn my love,

And I'll no longer be a Capulet.'

Juliet

'What's in a name? that which we call a rose
By any other name would smell as sweet;'

Juliet

'My bounty is as boundless as the sea,

My love as deep; the more I give to thee,

The more I have, for both are infinite.'

Juliet

'If that thy bent of love be honourable,
Thy purpose marriage, send me word to-morrow,'
Juliet

'Good night, good night! parting is such sweet sorrow,
That I shall say good night till it be morrow.'
Juliet

'Then hie you hence to Friar Laurence' cell.

There stays a husband to make you a wife.'

Nurse

'These violent delights have violent ends
And in their triumph die, like fire and powder,
Which, as they kiss, consume.'
Friar Laurence

'A plague o' both your houses!'

Mercutio

'I beg for justice, which thou, prince, must give;

Romeo slew Tybalt, Romeo must not live.'

Lady Capulet

'And for that offence

Immediately we do exile him hence . . .

... let Romeo hence in haste,

Else, when he's found, that hour is his last.'

Prince

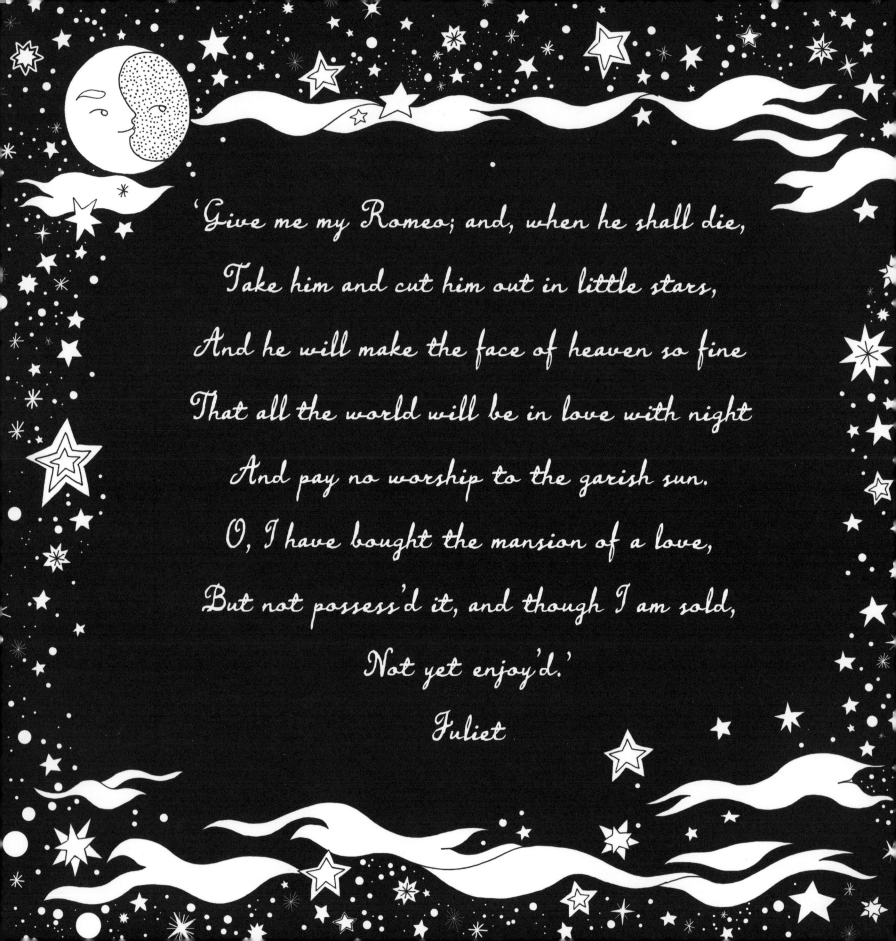

'Give me my Romeo; and, when he shall die,

Take him and cut him out in little stars,

And he will make the face of heaven so fine

That all the world will be in love with night

And pay no worship to the garish sun.

O, I have bought the mansion of a love,

But not possess'd it, and though I am sold,

Not yet enjoy'd.'

Juliet

'Wilt thou be gone? it is not yet near day:

It was the nightingale, and not the lark,

That pierced the fearful hollow of thine ear;

Nightly she sings on yon pomegranate-tree.

Believe me, love, it was the nightingale.'

Juliet

'O think'st thou we shall ever meet again?'

Juliet

'I doubt it not; and all these woes shall serve

For sweet discourses in our time to come.'

Romeo

'Marry, my child, early next Thursday morn,

The gallant, young and noble gentleman,

The County Paris, at Saint Peter's Church,

Shall happily make thee there a joyful bride.'

Lady Capulet

'O, sweet my mother, cast me not away!

Delay this marriage for a month, a week;

Or, if you do not, make the bridal bed

In that dim monument where Tybalt lies.'

Juliet

'Take thou this vial, being then in bed,

And this distilled liquor drink thou off;

When presently through all thy veins shall run

A cold and drowsy humour, for no pulse

Shall keep his native progress, but surcease:

No warmth, no breath, shall testify thou livest;

. . .

And in this borrow'd likeness of shrunk death

Thou shalt continue two and forty hours,

And then awake as from a pleasant sleep.'

Friar Laurence

'News from Verona!—How now, Balthasar!

Dost thou not bring me letters from the friar?

How doth my lady? Is my father well?

How fares my Juliet? that I ask again;

Romeo

'Then she is well, and nothing can be ill:
Her body sleeps in Capel's monument,
And her immortal part with angels lives.'
Balthasar

'Well, Juliet, I will lie with thee to-night

...let me have

A dram of poison,'

Romeo

'... drink it off; and, if you had the strength
Of twenty men, it would dispatch you straight.'

Apothecary

'O my love! my wife!

Death, that hath suck'd the honey of thy breath,

Hath had no power yet upon thy beauty.'

Romeo

'Here's to my love! O true apothecary!

Thy drugs are quick. Thus with a kiss I die.'

Romeo

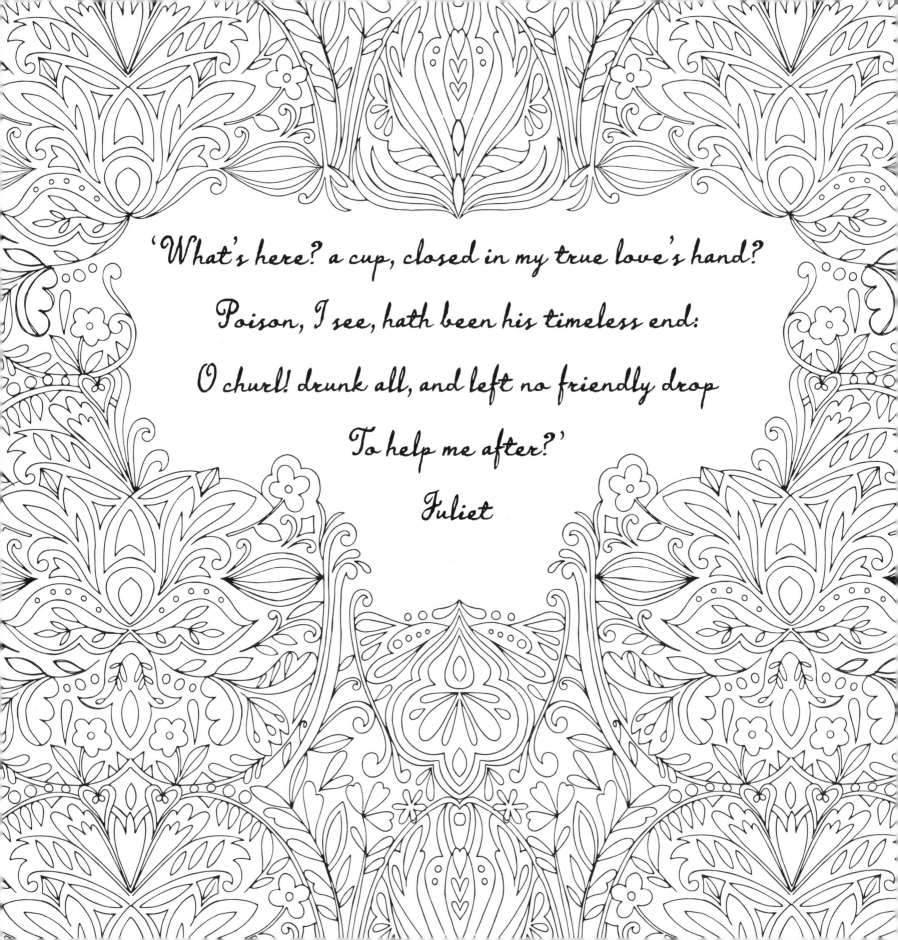

'What's here? a cup, closed in my true love's hand?

Poison, I see, hath been his timeless end:

O churl! drunk all, and left no friendly drop

To help me after?'

Juliet

'O happy dagger!

This is thy sheath; there rust, and let me die.'

Juliet

'See, what a scourge is laid upon your hate,

That heaven finds means to kill your joys with love.

And I for winking at your discords too

Have lost a brace of kinsmen: all are punish'd.'

Prince

'For I will raise her statue in pure gold;

That while Verona by that name is known,

There shall no figure at such rate be set

As that of true and faithful Juliet.'

Montague

'As rich shall Romeo's by his lady's lie;

Poor sacrifices of our enmity!'

Capulet

Juliet

Romeo

'A glooming peace this morning with it brings;

The sun, for sorrow, will not show his head:

Go hence, to have more talk of these sad things;

Some shall be pardon'd, and some punished.'

Prince

'For never was a story of more woe
Than this of Juliet and her Romeo.'

Prince

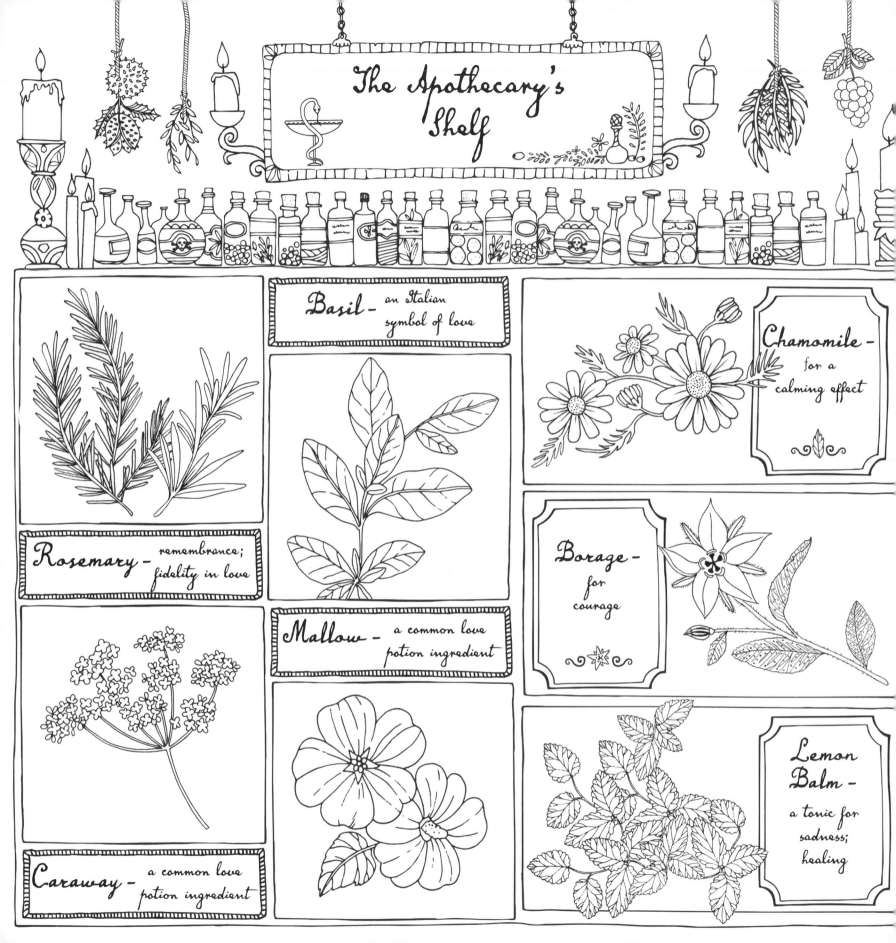

The Apothecary's Shelf

Basil – an Italian symbol of love

Chamomile – for a calming effect

Rosemary – remembrance; fidelity in love

Borage – for courage

Mallow – a common love potion ingredient

Caraway – a common love potion ingredient

Lemon Balm – a tonic for sadness; healing

Monkshood –
Romeo's deadly poison

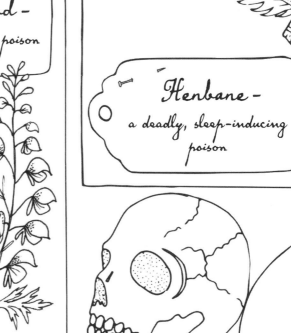

Henbane –
a deadly, sleep-inducing poison

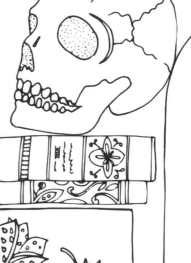

Deadly Nightshade –
Juliet's sleeping potion

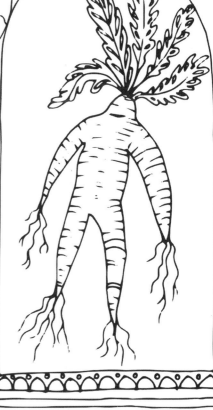

Thyme –
for bravery in battle

Wormwood –
for weaning infants

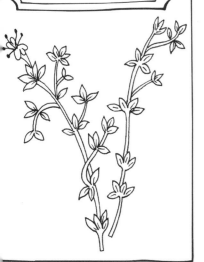

Thorn Apple –
a poison; sedative;
hallucinogenic;
a salve for burns

Mandrake root –
a poison; emetic;
hallucinogenic
and narcotic